Marvin Books

Marvin Steps Out
Marvin Born to Be Wild
Marvin Spoil Me

Published by POCKET BOOKS

Most Pocket Books are available at special quantity discounts for bulk purchases for sales promotions, premiums or fund raising. Special books or book excerpts can also be created to fit specific needs.

For details write the office of the Vice President of Special Markets, Pocket Books, 1230 Avenue of the Americas, New York, New York 10020.

Marvin

Spoil Me!

Tom Armstrong

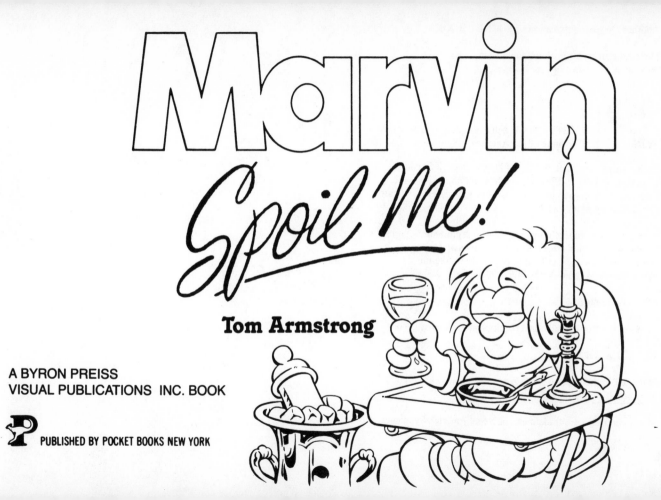

A BYRON PREISS
VISUAL PUBLICATIONS INC. BOOK

PUBLISHED BY POCKET BOOKS NEW YORK

Another *Original* publication of POCKET BOOKS

The comic strips in this book have been
previously published in syndication.

POCKET BOOKS, a division of Simon & Schuster, Inc.
1230 Avenue of the Americas, New York, N.Y. 10020

ISBN: 0-671-60705-7

First Pocket Books trade paperback printing August, 1986

10 9 8 7 6 5 4 3 2 1

Printed in the U.S.A.

Turkey and Dressing

Vichyssoise Flambé

Marvin

Spoil Me!

MARVIN, IF YOU KEEP SUCKING YOUR THUMB...

YOU'RE LIABLE TO WEAR IT AWAY

THAT'S OKAY...

I HAVE NO IMMEDIATE PLANS ON BECOMING A HITCHHIKER

TOM ARMSTRONG

YOU'VE HEARD OF THE ARMCHAIR QUARTERBACK

WELL, NOW MEET...

TOM ARMSTRONG

THE BASSINET QUARTERBACK

TACKLE THAT SUCKER

BOY, DISNEY WORLD SURE IS CROWDED

I KNOW! I DON'T HAVE ANY IDEA WHICH WAY TO GO

NOW I KNOW WHY THEY CALL THESE PLACES BEMUSEMENT PARKS

THIS LOOKS LIKE A GOOD PLACE TO STOP

The Cabana Inn

VACANCY

DID YOU FOLKS ENJOY DISNEY WORLD AND EPCOT?

HOW'D HE KNOW WE WENT THERE?

TOM ARMSTRONG

WHEN I GOT OUT OF COLLEGE, MY FIRST JOB WAS AS A "GO-FER" IN A LARGE COMPANY

BUT IN NINE YEARS I MANAGED TO WORK MY WAY UP TO AN EXECUTIVE POSITION

THEN I GAVE IT ALL UP TO BECOME A "GO-FER" AGAIN

WAH

TOM ARMSTRONG

I MISS THE FREEDOM I HAD BEFORE MARVIN CAME ALONG

SOMETIMES I FEEL LIKE A PRISONER...

DRAGGING MY BALL AND CHAIN AROUND

I RESENT THAT

TOM ARMSTRONG

EVERYBODY IN THIS FAMILY HAS A JOB TO DO, MARVIN

DADDY WORKS IN AN OFFICE, MOMMY TAKES CARE OF YOU AND OUR HOME...

AND YOUR JOB IS TO BE A GOOD BABY

I WANT A RAISE

TOM ARMSTRONG

WAH

TOM ARMSTRONG

DOO-WAH-P DOO-WAH-P

EVERY ONCE IN A WHILE I LIKE TO MIX A LITTLE FIFTIES SOUND INTO MY REPERTOIRE

WHAT SEEMS TO BE MARVIN'S PROBLEM, MRS. MILLER?

HE'S JUST BEEN SO QUIET THE LAST COUPLE OF DAYS, DR. TWITT

WELL, LET'S TAKE A LOOK IN HIS MOUTH WITH THE OL' TONGUE DEPRESSOR

HMMM...JUST AS I SUSPECTED...HE HAS A **DEPRESSED TONGUE**

I WONDER IF THE A.M.A. KNOWS HENNY YOUNGMAN IS PRACTICING WITHOUT A LICENSE?

TOM ARMSTRONG

I DON'T KNOW, DOCTOR TWITT, MARVIN JUST HASN'T BEEN HIMSELF LATELY

SEEMS LIKE A DIFFERENT PERSON, HUH?

SOUNDS LIKE THE "RICH LITTLE" SYNDROME

WANT TO SEE ME DO AN IMPRESSION OF YOU? QUACK! QUACK!

TOM ARMSTRONG

WAAAAH!

HERE'S YOUR BOTTLE, MARVIN

TOM ARMSTRONG

BABIES ARE SELDOM HAPPY UNTIL THEY'VE FOUND INNER PEACE

SLURP SLURP

IT'S NOT SOMETHING THAT I NORMALLY GIVE MUCH THOUGHT TO...

BUT EVERY SO OFTEN SOMETHING HAPPENS THAT FORCES ME TO FACE MY OWN MORTALITY

TOM ARMSTRONG

LIKE BUYING MY FIRST PAIR OF "MATURE CUT" JEANS

SOME PLANTS ARE OUTDOOR PLANTS...

AND SOME PLANTS ARE INDOOR PLANTS

THE INDOOR ONES HAVE TO BE POTTY TRAINED

I CAN'T BELIEVE HOW FAST THIS HOUSE GETS DIRTY

POLIS

I BARELY FINISH CLEANING IT, AND IT'S TIME TO START ALL OVER AGAIN

SPRIT!

TOM ARMSTRONG

THIS PLACE IS FULL OF DUST COLLECTORS!

EVERYBODY NEEDS A HOBBY

I CAN'T WAIT FOR SUMMER TO GET HERE

JENNY, I'VE DECIDED THAT THIS YEAR I'M GOING TO PLANT A GARDEN

THEN EVERY NIGHT THIS SUMMER WE'LL HAVE **FRESH VEGETABLES** FROM OUR VERY OWN BACKYARD

LEAVE IT TO DAD TO RUIN A PERFECTLY GOOD SEASON

TOM ARMSTRONG

"HOW TO GROW A PERFECT VEGETABLE GARDEN- STEP 1: GROUND-BREAKING"

HMMMM...I WONDER WHAT KIND OF TOOL I SHOULD USE TO BREAK UP THE GROUND?

HOW ABOUT A GARDEN CLUB?

TOM ARMSTRONG

"HOW TO GROW A PERFECT VEGETABLE GARDEN - CHAPTER ELEVEN:"

LAWN YUMMYS

"THE FINAL STEP TO A SUCCESSFUL GARDEN IS SPREADING THE FERTILIZER"

AT LAST SOMETHING DAD HAS SOME EXPERIENCE IN...

LAWN YUMMYS

HE WORKS FOR AN ADVERTISING AGENCY

THERE, MARVIN, OUR VEGETABLE GARDEN IS ALL PLANTED

AND IT FILLS ME WITH A DEEP SENSE OF PRIDE TO PRODUCE SOMETHING WITH MY OWN TWO HANDS

I THINK I KNOW JUST HOW OUR FOREFATHERS WHO FOUNDED THIS GREAT COUNTRY MUST HAVE FELT

OUCH!

DID THEY HAVE SORE BACKS, TOO?

TOM ARMSTRONG

I WISH I COULD REMEMBER WHERE I LEFT MY MARBLES

I KNOW

IN THE DRIVEWAY

TOM ARMSTRONG

I'LL SURE BE GLAD WHEN IT GETS WARM ENOUGH...

SO THAT BITSY CAN SLEEP OUTSIDE AT NIGHT

TOM ARMSTRONG

I'M GETTING TIRED OF HIM HOWLING AT MY NIGHT-LIGHT

AHROOO!

THERE'S AN INTERESTING STORY BEHIND HOW YOU GOT THAT STUFFED BUNNY, MARVIN

ON THE DAY YOU WERE BORN, I ASKED YOUR FATHER TO GO BUY YOU YOUR FIRST TOY

I WANTED IT TO BE SOMETHING THAT WOULD BE WARM AND CUDDLY AND GIVE YOU A FEELING OF SECURITY

YOUR FATHER WANTED TO GET YOU A FOOTBALL

ON THE DAY YOU WERE BORN YOUR FATHER WENT OUT TO BUY YOUR FIRST TOY...

I HOPE MARVIN LIKES THE STUFFED BUNNY I GOT HIM

NOW IF I CAN JUST GET THIS DOOR OPEN ...OOPS

SPITAL

UH, OH...

TOM ARMSTRONG

TOM ARMSTRONG

THOSE "ABOVE GROUND" POOLS ARE REALLY GETTING POPULAR

IT NEVER FAILS

IT ALWAYS STARTS TO RAIN...

THE MINUTE YOU PUT THE TOP DOWN

TOM ARMSTRONG

SOME DAYS IT JUST DOESN'T SEEM LIKE I'LL EVER GET TO THE BOTTOM OF MARVIN'S DIAPERS

CHUGA CHUGA

CHUGA CHUGA

NO PUN INTENDED

CHUGA CHUGA

One, two, Velcro my shoe;

Three, four, Ring at the door;

WHY DO I GET THE FEELING THIS IS A REVISED EDITION?

TOM ARMSTRONG

WE GO THROUGH THIS EVERY DAY, MARVIN

WAH!

WHY MUST YOU ALWAYS THROW A BIG TANTRUM WHEN I TELL YOU IT'S TIME FOR YOUR NAP?

POUND! POUND!

THINK OF IT AS THE STORM BEFORE THE QUIET

TOM ARMSTRONG

MOM'S NOT NORMALLY CLUMSY...

TOM ARMSTRONG

BUT I'VE NOTICED THAT WHENEVER SHE MAKES ME A BOTTLE...

SHE ALWAYS SEEMS TO SPILL A LITTLE ON HER WRIST

SPLURT SPLURT

RATS. WE'RE ALL OUT OF CREAM FOR MY COFFEE

SPLOOT!

UH...THANKS, MARVIN

WHAT'S MINE IS YOURS

TOM ARMSTRONG

I DON'T KNOW...

I'M NOT SURE I LIKE THESE NEW NEON DIAPERS

TOM ARMSTRONG

UH...MAY I ASK WHAT MARVIN IS DOING WITH HIS DIAPER TIED AROUND HIS HEAD?

HE DOES THAT EVERY TIME "THE BOSS" COMES ON MTV

BORN IN THE USA

TOM ARMSTRONG

YOU KNOW IT'S TIME TO GO ON A DIET...

WHEN YOU GET GRASS STAINS ON YOUR STOMACH

TOM ARMSTRONG

HELLO, JENNY? THIS IS YOUR OLD BOSS, STEVE COLEMAN

OH, HI, STEVE

TOM ARMSTRONG

I'M NOT INTERRUPTING ANYTHING IMPORTANT, AM I?

WAH!

THE REASON I'M CALLING, JENNY, IS THAT WE REALLY NEED YOU TO COME BACK TO WORK

I'VE GOT TO TELL YOU, YOU REALLY LEFT YOUR MARK ON THIS COMPANY

THEY JUST CAN'T GET ALONG WITHOUT YOU, JENNY GIRL

BECAUSE OF THE EXAMPLE YOU SET, FIVE WOMEN IN OUR OFFICE ARE GOING ON MATERNITY LEAVE

TOM ARMSTRONG

TIC TOC

GROWL!

TIC TOC

MUST BE LUNCH TIME

TOM ARMSTRONG

FOR THE FIRST FEW MONTHS OF MY LIFE I THOUGHT I HAD A PROBLEM WITH MY HEARING

I HAD A CONSTANT CLICKING NOISE IN MY EAR

THEN I REALIZED IT WAS JUST DAD TAKING PICTURES

CLICK! CLICK! CLICK!

TOM ARMSTRONG

 **M-I-C-** SEE YOU REAL SOON! MOM SAYS THESE ARE OLD SHOWS...

 **K-E-Y-** WHY? BECAUSE WE LIKE YOU!! AND THAT THE MOUSEKETEERS HAVE ALL GROWN BIG

M-O-U-S-EEEE I GUESS THEY'RE RATKETEERS NOW

TOM ARMSTRONG

 OOOF!

 I'M SUCH A CLUMSY CRAWLER

 I MUST HAVE BEEN BORN WITH TWO LEFT KNEES

TOM ARMSTRONG

TAP!

PLOP!

FLING!

TOM ARMSTRONG

SO YOU WERE THE ONE WHO THREW DAD'S GOLF BALL BACK OUT OF THE HOLE

THAT'S RIGHT

WHAT'S A MOLE DOING LIVING IN THE FOURTEENTH HOLE?

TOM ARMSTRONG

I ALWAYS WANTED A HOME THAT OVERLOOKED A GOLF COURSE

ISN'T IT KIND OF DANGEROUS FOR A MOLE TO LIVE IN THE FOURTEENTH HOLE OF A GOLF COURSE?

NOT USUALLY...

EXCEPT FOR THE TIME I RAISED UP OUT OF THE HOLE JUST AS THE GROUNDS-KEEPER WAS MOWING THE GREEN...

I LOOKED LIKE MR. T FOR A MONTH

TOM ARMSTRONG

DOESN'T IT SOMETIMES GET A LITTLE COLD AT NIGHT LIVING OUT HERE ON A GOLF COURSE?

WHEN IT DOES, I SIMPLY BUILD A CAMPFIRE...

WITH ALL THOSE LITTLE BROKEN TEES THE GOLFERS LEAVE BEHIND

TOM ARMSTRONG

ACTUALLY, IT'S PRETTY QUIET LIVING ON A GOLF COURSE DURING THE WEEK

BUT ON THE WEEKENDS...

THERE'S MORE DOUBLE-KNIT POLYESTER AROUND HERE THAN YOU CAN SHAKE A STICK AT

Tom Armstrong

I THOUGHT MOLES WERE SUPPOSED TO LIVE IN HOLES THEY DUG IN THE GROUND

YEAH, I USED TO...

BUT I GOT TIRED OF THE "RUSTIC" LOOK

Tom Armstrong

COME ON, MARVIN, JUST TRY A BITE OF YOUR STRAINED BROCCOLI

PLPLPLPL!

SOME PEOPLE JUST CAN'T TAKE "NO" FOR AN ANSWER

TOM ARMSTRONG

THERE, A FRESH BAKED CHOCOLATE CAKE FOR THE PARTY TONIGHT

I SURE HOPE YOU AREN'T PLANNING ON TRYING TO STEAL A PIECE THE MINUTE MY BACK IS TURNED, MARVIN

TOM ARMSTRONG

I'M NOT SAYING MARVIN HAS A BAD TEMPER...

BUT WE MEASURE HIS TANTRUMS ON A RICHTER SCALE

WAAH

DAD'S WEARING HIS SPECIAL SHOES THAT MAKE THOSE FUNNY NOISES ON THE KITCHEN FLOOR

SQUEAK

SQUEAK

I THINK THEY'RE CALLED "SQUEAKERS"

SQUEAK

SQUEAK

TOM ARMSTRONG

Ship Shape Spa

MOM'S BEEN GOING TO A FITNESS CENTER TO GET IN SHAPE

SHE PUTS ME IN THE NURSERY WHILE SHE WORKS OUT

WOULD YOU LIKE A LITTLE SNACK, HONEY?

MOM'S LOST THREE POUNDS AND I'VE GAINED FOUR

COOKIES

TOM ARMSTRONG

EVERY NIGHT DAD DOES TWENTY SIT-UPS

OOMP!

I DON'T KNOW WHY HE HAS TO PRACTICE SO MUCH

I'VE BEEN ABLE TO SIT UP GOOD SINCE I WAS THREE MONTHS OLD

PANT! PANT!

TOM ARMSTRONG

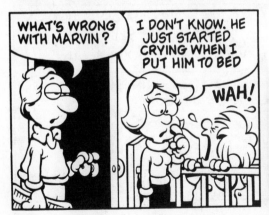

NOW I'VE SEEN EVERYTHING. DAD BOUGHT BITSY A TREADMILL...

SO HE COULD CHASE HIM WHILE HE RIDES HIS EXERCISE BIKE

ARF! ARF!

Tom Armstrong

SOMETIMES I THINK MY LIFE IS IN A RUT

EVERY MORNING IT'S THE SAME OLD THING... I WAKE UP CRYING, GET MY DIAPER CHANGED, DRINK A BOTTLE, BURP AND GO BACK TO SLEEP

TOMORROW I'M GOING TO DO SOMETHING REALLY DIFFERENT

I'M GOING TO WAKE UP, GET MY DIAPER CHANGED, DRINK A BOTTLE, BURP AND CRY MYSELF BACK TO SLEEP

Tom Armstrong

FIRST, ALL THE FITNESS EXPERTS SAID JOGGING WAS GOOD FOR YOU

NOW THEY SAY JOGGING IS BAD, BUT WALKING IS GOOD

I FIGURE WHEN THEY GET AROUND TO THE BENEFITS OF CRAWLING I'LL HAVE IT ACED

I WISH YOU'D HOLD STILL, MARVIN

INSTEAD OF CALLING THESE THINGS CHANGING PADS...

WIGGLE KICK SQUIRM

THEY SHOULD CALL THEM LAUNCHING PADS

TOM ARMSTRONG

JUST WHAT DO YOU THINK YOU'RE DOING, YOUNG MAN?!

WELL, USUALLY I DRAW PICTURES ON PAPER AND YOU PUT THEM ON THE FRONT OF THE REFRIGERATOR

I JUST THOUGHT I'D CUT OUT THE MIDDLE STEP

TOM ARMSTRONG

?

MUST BE AIR MAIL

TOM ARMSTRONG

Cartoonist Tom Armstrong is by no means a newcomer to the art field. At the ripe old age of five he drew a comic strip about camels, and from those humble beginnings sprang the comic genius behind Tom's later—and more human—syndicated cartoon creations, MARVIN and JOHN DARLING.

"I started cartooning probably before I could talk," Tom says. "My dad was an aspiring cartoonist, and after watching him for a while, I started drawing, too."

After four years of high school art training, Tom entered the University of Evansville, serving as the staff cartoonist for the campus paper, The Crescent, with a weekly strip about campus life called "Two-S." He graduated with a bachelor's degree in fine arts and several art awards under his belt: the Helen Morris Outstanding Senior Award in oil painting, the University of Evansville alumni Certificate of Excellence, the Medal of Merit for "significant contributions to collegiate journalism," second place for Best Editorial Cartoons from the Pi Delta Epsilon national journalism fraternity and the Indiana Collegiate Press Association's Best Editorial Cartoon award.

From there, Tom got into free-lance illustrating: He's drawn for many well-known publications, including **The Saturday Evening Post** and **The National Review**.

Tom has also done a good deal of work with advertising agencies, developing animated cartoons, multi-media slide presentations, animated TV spots and print ads for national companies from RCA to Sears and many more. He is a three-time recipient of the Golden Circle Award for "achieving the highest standards of advertising and selling excellence in worldwide competition."

Tom's first venture into comic strip syndication came in 1979 with JOHN DARLING, done in tandem with FUNKY WINKERBEAN creator Tom Batiuk. DARLING stars a fictional TV talk show host, his co-workers and celebrity guests (real-life celebrities drawn in caricature by Armstrong).

MARVIN, featuring the precocious red-haired star of Marvin Steps Out, followed in August, 1982. The character's popularity on the comics pages soon led to equal success in licensing and merchandising.

A prime-time television special, produced by Southern Star Studios, is in production for CBS.

Tom, his wife, Glenda, and two children, Jonathan and Jennifer (who also serve as a gold mine of ideas for MARVIN's antics) make their home in southern Indiana.